Let's Read!

📖 Read the Page

▶ Read the Story

⭐ Game

◆ Sound It / Say It

↻ Repeat

⏹ Stop

Get-Ready Words

antenna	launch
catapult	Lookout
command	magnet
excited	rescue
helicopter	robot

The Great Robot Rescue

The pups are excited.
Ryder has built a robot dog.

He calls it Robo Dog.

Ryder can give
Robo Dog commands.

2

Ryder says,
"Walk, Robo Dog!"

Robo Dog barks and
starts to walk.

4

Ryder can make
Robo Dog dig.

Ryder can make
Robo Dog fly.

"Robo Dog can run superfast!"
Ryder tells the pups.

Marshall wants to race Robo Dog.

Chase yells, "On your marks, get set, go!"

Marshall runs so fast,
he bumps into Ryder.

Ryder falls on Robo Dog!

Now Robo Dog's antenna
is bent and broken.

Robo Dog goes out of control!

He flies all over town and makes a big mess.

"PAW Patrol, to the Lookout!" Ryder cries.

The pups rush into the Lookout.

"Ready for action, Ryder sir!"
says Chase.

"Robo Dog is broken," Ryder says.
We need to catch him so we can fix him.
We also need to clean up the town."

📖 Ryder has a plan.

"PAW Patrol is on a roll!" Ryder cries.

Skye flies in her helicopter. She looks for Robo Dog.

The rest of the pups clean up Robo Dog's mess.

Rocky builds a catapult.
It will launch a magnet.

The magnet will stick
to Robo Dog.

Skye will use her hook
to grab the magnet.

Rocky fires the catapult.

"Perfect shot, Rocky!" Ryder says.

Skye grabs Robo Dog with the hook!

Skye lowers Robo Dog to the ground.

"Sorry, buddy," Ryder says.

He shuts off Robo Dog.

 Rocky has an idea. "I have an old antenna," he says. "I think it will work."

Ryder tries it. It works!

"Thanks, pups!" says Ryder.

Rocky and all the pups bark,
"If you're ever in trouble,
just yelp for help!"

Words You're Learning

Short Vowels

Short a Words	Short e Words	Short i Words	Short o Words	Short u Words
and	bent	big	dog	bumps
can	get	dig	off	just
fast	help	fix	on	pups
grab	mess	him	shot	run
plan	yelp	will		up

Long Vowels

Long a Words	Long e Words	Long i Words	Long o Words	Long u Words
make	clean	cries	go	use
race	he	flies	goes	
	need	fires	so	
	she	tries		
	we			

Sight Words

a	have	says	wants
also	into	the	work
are	of	to	your
built	old	walk	you're
give	ready